"THE CRACKED EGG SERIES"

TEN FUN WAYS TO COME OUT OF YOUR SHELL

"Unique activities to help promote positive thinking."

BOOK ONE

written and illustrated by
LINDA C. BRYANT

 LC Productions

Ten Fun Ways to Come Out of Your Shell
Copyright © 1992 by Linda C. Bryant

LC Productions
119-5th Street, Suite B-101
Wenatchee, WA 98801
800-274-2310

Printed and bound in the United States of America.
Also available in French, German, Japanese, Russian and Spanish.

Library of Congress No. 92-85112

ISBN #1-881232-01-8

Books by Linda C. Bryant

"The Cracked Egg Series"
Ten Fun Ways to Come Out of Your Shell
Ten Fun Ways to Feel Better About Yourself
Ten Fun Ways to View the Real You
Ten Fun Ways to Create the Magic in You

Upcoming Series by Linda C. Bryant

"Talents Unlimited for Kids"
"Out of Your Shell and Shining Bright"

This series is dedicated to ...

Christopher Michael (Chris) and
Jonathan Paul (Jon) —
my sons, and two of my best friends.

Table of Contents

Note to the 'Adult Kid' or Parent...

This book can help you to further understand positive thinking and begin to have the physical results of its process quickly and simply.

The techniques are simple to use. You will enjoy integrating the ways into your own routine and assist your children or someone close to you in developing this understanding.

The format is designed to be used every day for 30 days. The book's size allows you to carry it and have it handy to use. Writing and filling in the pages is very important in the technique and results. Do it for you — you'll be glad you did. Trust and do it, you will know why in a month! I will guarantee positive results with the applied methods. The quality depends solely on you. It is worth more than I can possibly say to complete this book. Give yourself what you deserve in life — the rewards are great!

My best to you, have fun.

Linda

Just for Kids . . .

This book has made it into your hands to have fun learning how positive thinking and acting works in your life. The results depend on you doing these ways every day for just 30 days to begin with.

I know some of you will want some help with doing this. Get it.

Some of you may simply find this book as a diary of sorts to help you with just you, and it will do just that, positively. Whatever way you choose is great, as long as you have fun doing it.

No matter who you are or what you are doing, your life can be positively more fun. It is important to write it down and keep track. I can only say you will know why in 30 days. So what the heck, do it and get a lot of positive surprises this month!

Have fun.

Linda

HOW TO USE THIS BOOK !

1. ATTITUDE CHECK-IN
2. RULES OF THE ROAD
3. THE 'NO NEED TO BUY' SUPPLY LIST
4. BUDDY-UP !

GO

~ 1 ~

ATTITUDE

LOVE LIFE & HAVE FUN !

(This is not a chore.)

BE UPBEAT and HAPPY !

(Even if you have to practice this at first,
the more you do it, the easier it gets.)

CHALLENGE YOURSELF !

(Go through the entire day
using this new attitude.)

~ 2 ~

RULES OF THE ROAD:

FUN

FUN

FUN

DO ALL THE STEPS EVERYDAY !

(Remember – WHO WANTS A DAY OFF FROM FUN ?)

Fill in one line per day.

~ 3 ~

THE 'NO NEED TO BUY' SUPPLY LIST

IF YOU DO NOT HAVE ANY OF THE FOLLOWING, BORROW FROM SOMEONE THAT DOES:

1. A big mirror you can use by yourself at least two (2) times a day.

2. Pen or pencil to write daily in your book. (The more you write in it, the more good comes from it !)

~ 4 ~

BUDDY-UP !

1. Get a good 'friend' and do some of the 'ways' together. Sharing these things about you helps them to know you better and you them.

2. Get an 'adult' you care about to do this with you ! ! !

GO FOR IT

and

LET THE FUN BEGIN !

LIST THINGS YOU WOULD LIKE BETTER OR CHANGED IN YOUR LIFE.

(This is for future reference.)

★ _get better at soccer_ ★ _____

»→ _____ »→ _____

! _____ ! _____

♥ _____ ♥ _____

★ _____ ★ _____

»→ _____ »→ _____

! _____ ! _____

♥ _____ ♥ _____

★ _____ ★ _____

»→ _____ »→ _____

! _____ ! _____

♥ _____ ♥ _____

~ 1 ~

MIRROR, MIRROR

~ 1 ~

FIRST THING IN THE MORNING

as you get ready ...

LOOK IN THE MIRROR and SAY OUT LOUD —

"your name," I LOVE YOU. YOU ARE SPECIAL !

~ 1 ~

NOTES FOR YOU

Write down each day how you felt
when you said this to yourself.

(If you feel strange — write it !)
(If you feel great — write it !)

1. _____

2. _____

3. _____

4. _____

5. _____

6. _____

7. _____

8. _____

9. _____

10. _____

11. _____

12. _____

13. _____

14. _____

15. _____

MORE NOTES FOR YOU

Continue to write down each day
how you felt when you said this to yourself.

(Watch the change take place in you !)

16. _____

17. _____

18. _____

19. _____

20. _____

21. _____

22. _____

23. _____

24. _____

25. _____

26. _____

27. _____

28. _____

29. _____

30. _____

This way to #2

~ 2 ~

TALK TO YOURSELF !

~ 2 ~

THINK A 'HAPPY THOUGHT' about WHAT it is you

LOVE about YOU and WHAT is so SPECIAL !

(looking in the mirror)

SAY IT OUT LOUD TO YOURSELF !

~ 2 ~

LIST <u>WHAT</u> YOU LOVE
ABOUT YOU !

Write it down — a new one each day.

1._____	16. _____
2._____	17. _____
3._____	18. _____
4._____	19. _____
5._____	20. _____
6._____	21. _____
7._____	22. _____
8._____	23. _____
9._____	24. _____
10._____	25. _____
11._____	26. _____
12._____	27. _____
13._____	28. _____
14._____	29. _____
15._____	30. _____

~ 2 ~

LIST WHAT YOU THOUGHT
SPECIAL ABOUT YOU TODAY !

Write it down — a new one each day.

1. _____

2. _____

3. _____

4. _____

5. _____

6. _____

7. _____

8. _____

9. _____

10. _____

11. _____

12. _____

13. _____

14. _____

15. _____

16. _____

17. _____

18. _____

19. _____

20. _____

21. _____

22. _____

23. _____

24. _____

25. _____

26. _____

27. _____

28. _____

29. _____

30. _____

This way to #3

~ 3 ~

LOOK IN YOUR HEART !

~ 3 ~

LOOK IN YOUR HEART.
Be thankful for what you
already have, so more
can come your way.

LIST 3 different things each
day that you are thankful you
have and watch the list grow.

SAY, "Thank you" out loud to
3 different people today !

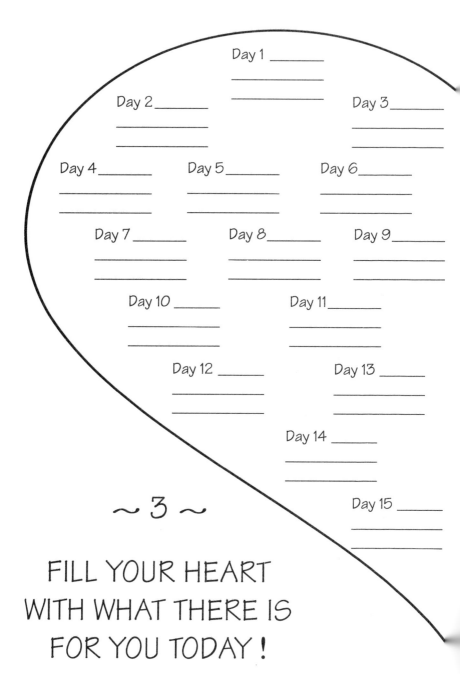

Day 1 _____
_____

Day 2 _____
_____
_____

Day 3 _____
_____
_____

Day 4 _____
_____
_____

Day 5 _____
_____
_____

Day 6 _____
_____
_____

Day 7 _____
_____
_____

Day 8 _____
_____
_____

Day 9 _____
_____
_____

Day 10 _____
_____
_____

Day 11 _____
_____
_____

Day 12 _____
_____
_____

Day 13 _____
_____
_____

Day 14 _____
_____
_____

Day 15 _____
_____
_____

~ 3 ~

FILL YOUR HEART
WITH WHAT THERE IS
FOR YOU TODAY !

Fill the whole page with an extra or two. Watch it
grow full as the days pass !

Day 16 _____
_____

Day 17 _____
_____
_____

Day 18 _____
_____
_____

Day 19 _____
_____
_____

Day 20 _____
_____
_____

Day 21 _____
_____
_____

Day 22 _____
_____
_____

Day 23 _____
_____
_____

Day 24 _____
_____
_____

Day 25 _____
_____
_____

Day 26 _____
_____
_____

Day 27 _____
_____
_____

Day 28 _____
_____
_____

Day 29 _____
_____
_____

Day 30 _____
_____
_____

This way to #4

~ 4 ~

HUG A TREE

~ 4 ~

HUG A TREE
SO TIGHT YOU SQUEEZE
THE 'SAP' OUT OF IT !

Find a new one each day
— or a favorite one —
special to you.

(Substitute 'something' of your choice
if no trees are near you.)

~ 4 ~

WHAT CAME TO MIND
just BEFORE you did this, or maybe
a question you thought of.
Write it down — a line each day.

1. _____
2. _____
3. _____
4. _____
5. _____
6. _____
7. _____
8. _____
9. _____
10. _____
11. _____
12. _____
13. _____
14. _____
15. _____

~ 4 ~

MORE NOTES TO YOURSELF
of what came to mind just
before you did this.
Write it down.

16. _____
17. _____
18. _____
19. _____
20. _____
21. _____
22. _____
23. _____
24. _____
25. _____
26. _____
27. _____
28. _____
29. _____
30. _____

~ 4 ~

AFTERWARDS what came to mind.
It may be a thought about a feeling,
an answer to a question, or an insight.

Write it down.

1. _____
2. _____
3. _____
4. _____
5. _____
6. _____
7. _____
8. _____
9. _____
10. _____
11. _____
12. _____
13. _____
14. _____
15. _____

~ 4 ~

MORE of what came to mind AFTERWARDS.

Write it down.

(Answers you seek come in many ways.)

16. _____

17. _____

18. _____

19. _____

20. _____

21. _____

22. _____

23. _____

24. _____

25. _____

26. _____

27. _____

28. _____

29. _____

30. _____

This way to #5

~ 5 ~

HUG A PET

~ 5 ~

DO JUST THAT —
HUG A PET !

Your own or someone else's

(You may want to leave pet goldfish out of this, but at least say 'Hi' to them !)

～ 5 ～

LIST PET'S NAME
or kind of pet you hugged !

(A visit to the pet store or
petting zoo will do here also.)

1._____   16. _____
2._____   17. _____
3._____   18. _____
4._____   19. _____
5._____   20. _____
6._____   21. _____
7._____   22. _____
8._____   23. _____
9._____   24. _____
10._____   25. _____
11._____   26. _____
12._____   27. _____
13._____   28. _____
14._____   29. _____
15._____   30. _____

~ 5 ~

PET'S REACTIONS:
Keep track (it's fun to watch).

How did they respond to you ?
Imagine what they may be thinking.

1. _____   16. _____
2. _____   17. _____
3. _____   18. _____
4. _____   19. _____
5. _____   20. _____
6. _____   21. _____
7. _____   22. _____
8. _____   23. _____
9. _____   24. _____
10. _____   25. _____
11. _____   26. _____
12. _____   27. _____
13. _____   28. _____
14. _____   29. _____
15. _____   30. _____

This way to #6

~ 6 ~

GIVE A BEAR HUG !

~ 6 ~

GIVE A BEAR HUG

TO SOMEONE YOU CARE FOR TODAY and FIND A DIFFERENT PERSON EVERYDAY FOR THE FUN OF IT.

(This will increase your list of friends !)

<u>WHO</u> DID YOU 'SURPRISE'
and give a bear hug to today ?

Write it down.

1._____	16. _____
2._____	17. _____
3._____	18. _____
4._____	19. _____
5._____	20. _____
6._____	21. _____
7._____	22. _____
8._____	23. _____
9._____	24. _____
10._____	25. _____
11._____	26. _____
12._____	27. _____
13._____	28. _____
14._____	29. _____
15._____	30. _____

~ 6 ~

PEOPLE'S REACTIONS.
Keep track.

What reaction did you get from these people ?
A hug back, a smile, a giggle, a sigh, a nice
word — watch !

1. _____   16. _____
2. _____   17. _____
3. _____   18. _____
4. _____   19. _____
5. _____   20. _____
6. _____   21. _____
7. _____   22. _____
8. _____   23. _____
9. _____   24. _____
10. _____   25. _____
11. _____   26. _____
12. _____   27. _____
13. _____   28. _____
14. _____   29. _____
15. _____   30. _____

This way to #7

~ 7 ~

LOOK, SMILE, SEND A BALLOON !

~ 7 ~

<u>LOOK</u> AT SOMEONE.

Notice who looks back at you.

<u>SMILE</u> AT THEM
and in your mind,

<u>SEND</u> them a 'pink' balloon
filled with LOVE.

~ 7 ~

LIST WHO —
It's fun to do this, even to people you may not even know!

List their name (if you know it) or describe
the person (e.g., lady walking a dog).

1._____   16. _____
2._____   17. _____
3._____   18. _____
4._____   19. _____
5._____   20. _____
6._____   21. _____
7._____   22. _____
8._____   23. _____
9._____   24. _____
10._____   25. _____
11._____   26. _____
12._____   27. _____
13._____   28. _____
14._____   29. _____
15._____   30. _____

~ 7 ~

WATCH THE REACTION
in these people.

The way they walk, sit, stand or smile. See how
many different changes you see this month.

1. _____	16. _____
2. _____	17. _____
3. _____	18. _____
4. _____	19. _____
5. _____	20. _____
6. _____	21. _____
7. _____	22. _____
8. _____	23. _____
9. _____	24. _____
10. _____	25. _____
11. _____	26. _____
12. _____	27. _____
13. _____	28. _____
14. _____	29. _____
15. _____	30. _____

This way to #8

～ 8 ～

IMPORTANT SECRET MISSION !

~ 8 ~

HERE IS YOUR ASSIGNMENT:

Do a job around the house, school or work area that no one asked you to do. No one has to know or say thank you at this time.

(This can be kept a secret just for you.)

Keep track —
More good will come to you & not always from who you did this good deed for.

~ 8 ~

WHAT DID YOU CHOOSE TO DO ?

Write it down.

1._____

2._____

3._____

4._____

5._____

6._____

7._____

8._____

9._____

10._____

11._____

12._____

13._____

14._____

15._____

16. _____

17. _____

18. _____

19. _____

20. _____

21. _____

22. _____

23. _____

24. _____

25. _____

26. _____

27. _____

28. _____

29. _____

30. _____

~ 8 ~

OBSERVE !

Watch and hear what reaction (if any) these people have. Did they 'happen to notice' what was done ? Keep them guessing for awhile !

(They may think there are magical little mice that help.)

1. _____   16. _____
2. _____   17. _____
3. _____   18. _____
4. _____   19. _____
5. _____   20. _____
6. _____   21. _____
7. _____   22. _____
8. _____   23. _____
9. _____   24. _____
10. _____   25. _____
11. _____   26. _____
12. _____   27. _____
13. _____   28. _____
14. _____   29. _____
15. _____   30. _____

This way to #9

~ 9 ~

A GIFT OF LOVE !

~ 9 ~

A GIFT OF LOVE —
A FUN WAY !

Tell someone around you today
something nice about
themselves !

(This is called a COMPLIMENT.)

Say it so they can 'hear' it ! !
When someone gives you a
compliment, say 'thank you' ! What
you give away <u>will</u> come back to you.

~ 9 ~

WHO DID YOU GIVE
A GIFT OF LOVE TO ?

(Write their name down.)

1. _____
2. _____
3. _____
4. _____
5. _____
6. _____
7. _____
8. _____
9. _____
10. _____
11. _____
12. _____
13. _____
14. _____
15. _____

~ 9 ~

MORE OF WHO YOU GAVE
A GIFT OF LOVE TO.

(List their name.)

16. _____

17. _____

18. _____

19. _____

20. _____

21. _____

22. _____

23. _____

24. _____

25. _____

26. _____

27. _____

28. _____

29. _____

30. _____

~ 9 ~

<u>WHAT IS IT</u> THAT YOU SAID ?

(Write out the compliment.)

1. _____
2. _____
3. _____
4. _____
5. _____
6. _____
7. _____
8. _____
9. _____
10. _____
11. _____
12. _____
13. _____
14. _____
15. _____

~ 9 ~

MORE OF WHAT YOU SAID.

(Write it out below.)

16. _____
17. _____
18. _____
19. _____
20. _____
21. _____
22. _____
23. _____
24. _____
25. _____
26. _____
27. _____
28. _____
29. _____
30. _____

This way to #10

~ 10 ~

POSITIVELY...GREAT!

~ 10 ~

LOOK IN THE MIRROR TONIGHT and

SAY (out loud) "your own name, YOU DID GREAT TODAY . . . TOMORROW — POSITIVELY — I WILL DO EVEN BETTER !"

Give yourself a hug good night.

~ 10 ~

WHAT DID YOU DO THAT WAS GREAT TODAY ?
What was better about it ?

Write it down.

BEFORE	TODAY	HOW WAS IT BETTER
e.g. Walked 2 miles	Walked 3 miles	1 mile further
1. _____	_____	_____
2. _____	_____	_____
3. _____	_____	_____
4. _____	_____	_____
5. _____	_____	_____
6. _____	_____	_____
7. _____	_____	_____
8. _____	_____	_____
9. _____	_____	_____
10. _____	_____	_____
11. _____	_____	_____
12. _____	_____	_____
13. _____	_____	_____
14. _____	_____	_____
15. _____	_____	_____

～ 10 ～

MORE OF WHAT YOU DID GREAT TODAY ?
What was better about it ?

Write it down.

BEFORE	TODAY	HOW WAS IT BETTER
e.g. Bench press 180 lbs.	190 lbs.	10 lbs. heavier
16. _____	_____	_____
17. _____	_____	_____
18. _____	_____	_____
19. _____	_____	_____
20. _____	_____	_____
21. _____	_____	_____
22. _____	_____	_____
23. _____	_____	_____
24. _____	_____	_____
25. _____	_____	_____
26. _____	_____	_____
27. _____	_____	_____
28. _____	_____	_____
29. _____	_____	_____
30. _____	_____	_____

~ 10 ~

ACCENT THE POSITIVE.

Write out a positive (happy) statement
to yourself for doing it better.
(E.g., I enjoy walking more each day.)

1. _____

2. _____

3. _____

4. _____

5. _____

6. _____

7. _____

8. _____

9. _____

10. _____

~ 10 ~

ACCENT THE POSITIVE
EVEN MORE !

(E.g., I am stronger and stronger every day.)

11. _____

12. _____

13. _____

14. _____

15. _____

16. _____

17. _____

18. _____

19. _____

20. _____

Keep going ! ⟫→

~ 10 ~

... AND MORE, POSITIVELY!

21. _____
_____
22. _____
_____
23. _____
_____
24. _____
_____
25. _____
_____
26. _____
_____
27. _____
_____
28. _____
_____
29. _____
_____
30. _____
_____

Watch great things happen for all the positive
thought seeds you planted in your life!!

From the Author...

That's me, Linda. I follow these techniques to make my life accomplishments fun and allow myself to perform a multitude of talented abilities developed over the years. The results I experienced (along with a lot of phone calls from people asking, "How do you do it?"), prompted me to write these books.

One important fact about me is that I encourage you to know about yourself. Those techniques are what I share in this series of books.

My life so far contains a lot of basics: Birth certificate from the state of Washington, report cards, driver's license, graduation diplomas, an official "press pass," and a first aid instructor's card — just to name a few. All these rites of passage have been great, including the one I gave myself, forming my own company — LC PRODUCTIONS.

Living and teaching what I take as a stand in life, that of wise self-reliance. I look forward to finding the cosmic chuckle in each new day. It's great!

May each of you look forward to finding the fun in life daily.

Linda C. Bryant

"THE CRACKED EGG SERIES"

Written and illustrated by Linda C. Bryant

UNIQUE NEW BOOKS — Individually focused —
Encourage breaking out of your shell
and promote progressive growth from wherever you are in life.

☐ Book 1 – TEN FUN WAYS TO COME OUT OF YOUR SHELL
"Unique activities to help promote positive thinking." *$11.95*

☐ Book 2 – TEN FUN WAYS TO FEEL BETTER ABOUT YOURSELF
"Encourages balanced well-being." *$11.95*

☐ Book 3 – TEN FUN WAYS TO VIEW THE REAL YOU
"Clarify and enjoy self-worth using your special talents." *$11.95*

☐ Book 4 – TEN FUN WAYS TO CREATE THE MAGIC IN YOU
"Believe in yourself & make your dreams come true." *$11.95*

LC Productions, 119-5th Street, Suite B-101, Wenatchee, WA 98801

Please send the items I have checked above. I am enclosing $_____.
(Add $1.00 plus $.50 each additional title for postage and handling. WA residents
add 7.9% sales tax.) Send check or money order, no cash or C.O.D.s please.

Name _____

Address _____

City/State _____ Zip _____

Daytime Phone (____) _____

☐ Visa   ☐ MasterCard

Exp. Date _____   Signature _____

Please allow 4-6 weeks for delivery.

All titles also available in French, German, Japanese, Russian and Spanish.
For pricing and ordering information, call 1-800-274-2130.

Prices and availability subject to change without notice.

NOTES